# Oh, Grandmother, What a Big Heart You Have

LOIS WYSE

A GARRET PRESS BOOK
DISTRIBUTED BY DOUBLEDAY & CO., INC.,
GARDEN CITY, NEW YORK.

**DESIGNED BY HERB LUBALIN**
**ILLUSTRATIONS BY ANTHONY SARIS**

LIBRARY OF CONGRESS CATALOG
CARD NUMBER: 72-75445
MANUFACTURED IN THE
UNITED STATES OF AMERICA

And we appreciate you!

## Call That Love

I have been taught
All homage is due
Those much older than I,
And so I respect you, Grandmother dear.

Call that manners.

But I have not been taught
The heart must fill and feel
Such tenderness for you.
And yet it does.

Call that love.

## Grandma's Bed

I crawl into your bed, Grandma,
And curl there like a question mark,
Yet I have no questions
Because you wrap your arms around me
And I know that
In your love I am warm.

## Thanks, Grandma, for Not Telling Me My Face Is Dirty, My Hair Is Too Long, and My Jeans Are Torn

It takes a special grace
Not to say the obvious.

## Sugar and Spice . . .

My grandmother's cookies taste of
     sugar and spice and chocolate chips
But the sweetest taste of all in granny's cookies
Is the love
That is baked in.

# Did You Bake Today, Grandma?

I'd rather eat spaghetti with you
Than chateaubriand with a king.
Of course, no king
Has invited me for chateaubriand lately.

# The Better To See You, Grandma

Look out this window, Grandma.
I think I see tomorrow.

# A Dozen Roses for My Grandmother

You are like these roses
That reach a time of God-given perfection.
How lucky for me that
I am here for that perfect time with you.

# The Duck Pond

Grandmother, come watch the ducks with me,
They sail across the pond
Proudly, white-thatched,
Trailing ducklings in their wake.

Come watch the ducks, Grandmother,
For they are so like you and me.

# Inheritance

China cupboards filled with cups of memories,
A piano that played in the days before me,
Secret drawers that hold my parents' past,
All these are here for me to see
And so piece together what has gone before
To understand the people who once
      walked these halls.

For in the home my grandmother created,
I find the beginnings of the love I have inherited.

# Why I Need You, Grandmother

Mothering is necessary,
But grandmothering
Is a luxury of life.